MW01088255

Team Baby

Creating a happy & rested family

Team *Baby*

The wisdom of Julia Dee
with Ida Gazzola

Creating a happy & rested family

Scepter

This book is not intended as a substitute for the medical advice of a physician. The reader should follow the suggestions contained in this book only under the advice of a competent physician and should regularly consult a physician with issues relating to the subject matter herein. The authors shall not be held liable for damages arising from the application of information contained in this book.

This is a reprint of Team Baby, originally published by Ida Gazzola, © 2012. This edition © Scepter Publishers, Inc., New York with permission. Team Baby, First Printing, December 2017.

Copyright © 2017 by Ida Gazzola

The total or partial reproduction of this book is not permitted nor its informatic treatment, or the transmission of any form or by any means, either electronic, mechanic, photocopy, or other methods without the prior written permission of the publisher.

Published by Scepter Publishers, Inc.

info@scepterpublishers.org
www.scepterpublishers.org
800-322-8773
New York

Scepter

All Rights Reserved.

Cover and Text Design and Layout by Christa Ledding
Cover Updates by Rose Design

ISBN: 9781594173257 (pbk)
9781594173295 (eBook)

Library of Congress Cataloging-in-Publication Data Names: Dee, Julia, author. | Gazzola, Ida, author. Title: Team baby : creating a happy and rested family / the wisdom of Julia Dee with Ida Gazzola. Description: New York : Scepter Publishers, Inc., [2017] | Reprint of Team Baby, originally published by Ida Gazzola, 2012. | Includes bibliographical references. Identifiers: LCCN 2017057368 (print) | LCCN 2017057773 (ebook) | ISBN 9781594173295 (ebook) | ISBN 9781594173257 (pbk) Subjects: LCSH: Newborn infants--Care. Classification: LCC RJ253 (ebook) | LCC RJ253 .D44 2017 (print) | DDC 649/.122--dc23 LC record available at https://lccn.loc.gov/2017057368

Printed in the United States of America

Table of *Contents*

Creating a happy & rested family

Babies are in my family—I come from a family of eleven. This schedule is the one I use, my mother used on us 11 kids and my grandmother used on her 11 kids. But the word 'schedule' may not describe it accurately. It is better thought of as mom and baby and dad working together as a team. The babies really thrive on this 'teamwork,' as the routine of feed, wake, and sleep gives them a sense of security. It also allows us moms to plan our day and to get things done. Your husband has to know how it works too, to support both of you and to participate in playing with baby while baby is gearing up for the last feed. I hope this will be a tool you can use as you develop your own family's rhythms.

—Julia

Julia's **Story**

Julia, her mother, and her grandmother have 32 babies between them. Through decades of mothering and by employing much common sense, their combined wisdom has developed a simple and practical routine for babies. Julia's own ten children slept through the night (6–8 hours) by one month and a good deal longer by the second month. This is the story of Julia's wonderful discovery. This story spans generations and is a living, breathing tale of babies and family life that we hope will inspire, provide encouragement *and* help you get some much-needed sleep.

To understand Julia's routine, it helps to understand Julia herself. This gentle and intuitive woman has a soft-spoken approach that belies her strength and wisdom. Julia is an insightful problem-solver and those skills form the basis of her recommended schedule.

Julia's advice rests on these key points

- babies are born with a stomach the size of a marble

- if the time between the baby's feeds is stretched, the baby will take more milk at each feed, prompting the stomach to grow

- the bigger a baby's stomach gets, the longer he can go between feeds

- the longer a baby can go between feeds (because he has all the milk he needs), the longer baby will sleep during the night

This is achieved by nursing both sides fully right from the first feed.

Nursing Each Side Fully Allows:

- the stomach to expand faster than feeding small amounts frequently, which also develops bad snacking habits

- the baby to learn how to have a full feed

- the routine of baby feeding every 3 hours (to start) to be established

- the mother's milk production to increase as the baby drinks more

This routine establishes full feeds and longer nap times (2–3 hours instead of cat naps), then gradually longer wake times and longer nighttime sleeps.

A mother's milk supply will adjust to demand. In other words, when the baby is hungrier, she demands more milk from your breasts and your body, in turn, will produce that milk. And milk is better produced when you are well-rested. Another huge benefit from feeding at regular times is decreased engorgement.

Note: Extraordinary things happen and health issues occur. If you or your baby has a serious health issue, please consult your doctor. The success of this routine depends on the good health of mother and child.

Before
Birth

Some preparation before the baby is born makes the transition much more smooth and enjoyable. Here are some ideas:

Meals

- Start a few months in advance and double or triple your family dinners, putting the extra in the freezer. You can also freeze crock pot meals in Ziploc bags.

- Ask older kids to choose a few meals that they like and have **them** make and freeze the meals in advance.

- Have your older children choose one or two meals to make after baby is born; and have the ingredients on hand.

- If freezer space is tight, make dry soups or other mason jar dry meal mixes.

- If someone offers to make meals for you or organize a meal train, take them up on it!

The Home

- Have extra help for the first week or two, whether friend, family or hired help.

- Prepare your husband to take a bigger role in arranging and managing the household for the first week (this is what Julia does).

- Set up a new chore schedule for the kids, explaining that extra help is needed when the baby arrives.

Sleep Exchange

- If you know someone who is pregnant or also has a new baby, arrange to alternately look after each other's older children so the mother with no children can take a nap!

Mental Preparation for Breastfeeding

- It takes a while to get used to breastfeeding any new baby, whether it is the first or fifth child. Mentally prepare for this feeding time before the baby is born. Some babies are quick feeders and some are extremely slow. Julia finds the average baby will feed twenty minutes one side and about seventeen on the second side. Plus there is the burping between sides and at the end. Be prepared for this 'resting time.' Have a comfortable chair, a big glass of water and a good book. It is a wonderful down-time for mother and baby to bond.

Julia finds this preparation is crucial for bonding with baby, setting the rhythm of baby and feeding, resting/sleeping, hormones settling, dealing with engorgement, pumping and so on. If things are organized in advance, it provides a quicker start to the feeding routines, mother's healing and regaining strength. Not everyone has this back up/family support, but if you can arrange this it will be a smoother transition. This can increase family contentment and possibly help with post partum depression.

Core
Principles

- **This feed schedule is *flexible*.** You design it to suit you and your family's needs. The whole idea is to put more order—and, by extension, more peace—in your life, so you can adjust the schedule when needed. For example, after the initial newborn stages, you can move the feed an hour earlier or later, depending on the commitments of the day, such as appointments, school pickup, activities, etc.

- *When the baby cries or makes a noise and it is not feeding time, it may not be necessary to pick him up right away*. It is surprising how long a baby can go at times just lying happily in the crib. If he is really fussing, see if it is something other than milk that he wants. Maybe a diaper change is required or maybe he needs to be burped. He could be too cold or too hot. Or maybe he just wants a change of position. Try a different baby chair or playpen. Sometimes he will just want a hug.

- *Wrap the baby snugly*, when putting her down to sleep. She will feel more secure in a womb-like environment. Julia highly recommends a bassinette (for babies 0–5 months) over a big crib because you can make it cozier and the blankets more tightly tucked. Again baby will feel very secure, there is less chance of flailing arms and she won't feel scared. This will help with extending the night sleep.

- *Help the baby to learn to sleep by herself
  (i.e. no 'sleep crutches')*

  - Don't rock her to sleep all the time—babies can be quite independent and soon they will learn how to fall asleep. If a baby is rocked to sleep and then wakes up alone in her bed, she might be upset by this change of environment.

  - If he falls asleep after a feed, especially the last feed, that is fine. Just make sure he is burped well. (See pages 32–36 for burping info.) However, some babies will keep sucking on the nipple for comfort and to soothe themselves to sleep. A mother can learn to recognize the difference between sucking for milk and sucking for comfort. If he is sucking for comfort, take him off the breast and, if it is bedtime, put him to bed. Sucking for comfort may not only establish a bad sleeping habit, but also may cause damage to the nipple.

  - Do not give the baby a soother at bedtime. Many babies will become dependent on their soother and then will cry every time it falls out. (See page 47 for more advice on soothers.)

- *Have the baby sleep in her own bed and in her own room if space permits.*

  - Sleeping in her own bed is key because you can become paranoid about squashing the baby and your sleep is not sound. Also, as the baby gets older, it will be harder for him to sleep in his own bed if he is used to sleeping in yours.

  - Sleeping in her own room is recommended because when the baby is in your room, you are more conscious of the baby's breathing and movements. You may be worried about waking her when the floor creaks or your husband snores, and so on, since some babies do wake up from those sorts of noises.

- One resourceful mother, who did not have a separate room for the baby in her townhouse, used her large walk-in closet as a temporary nursery. She put the bassinet in the closet for four months until she was comfortable enough to put the baby in her own room on a separate floor. In her words, "I just couldn't sleep with all that grunting and snorting."

- When a baby is used to being put down in the crib and then wakes up in the crib, this helps her develop the important ability to self-soothe or calm herself since she remembers that this is the place where she sleeps and she feels safe in that knowledge.

Dad is number one! Your husband and you form the basis of your family. Your unity is vitally important for your marriage and the happiness of the children. We moms can feel stronger emotionally towards our children, so we have to remind ourselves that our husband was our first choice. Sometimes a father can feel slighted if he perceives that the baby has taken his spot (whether in the bed or emotionally). Throughout all of this, keep in mind what is best not only for baby, but for Dad as well.

Always remember that the baby is constantly going through stages. Some stages are easy and others require more effort but, thankfully, each stage passes. Take baby steps instead of big strides and strive to implement a schedule. Your husband's support is very important, especially at the awake times. However, if this support is lacking, it is still very possible to work through the tough times and implement these principles.

Finally, not all mothers breastfeed. These scheduling suggestions can work equally well for bottle-fed babies.

The
Schedule

Below is the feeding schedule in point form. On page 12 each stage will be explained in more detail. In this schedule, the goal is the end result. It is important not to be discouraged when the process takes time as you work towards the final result.

Stage	Goal	Tips
Newborn	• Feed every 3 hours	• to get your milk flow coming in, which usually happens on Day 3 • do not wake baby in the night • feed from both breasts
4 or 5 days old	• Start stretching feeds to every 4 hours (day and night)	• wait 3 hrs, 15 minutes before feeding; then 3 hrs, 30 minutes, and so on • do 20 minutes awake time before last feed (see page 23)
1 week	• Push the middle of night feed later • Keep stretching time between feeds, working towards 4 hours apart	• use a nightly routine (see page 46 for further details) • do 20–30 minutes awake time before last feed (see page 23)

Stage	Goal	Tips
1 month	• Baby sleeps through night (6–7 hours from start of night feed to start of morning feed) • Keep stretching time between feeds, working towards 4 hours apart • 5 breastfeeds a day	• stretch feeds little by little as before • do 1 hour awake time before last feed (this continues to get longer day by day)
2–2.5 months	• Baby is sleeping between 8–12 hours • Stretch feeds to every 5 hrs during the day • 4 breastfeeds a day	• awake time before last feed is now the whole 5 hours (except maybe a 20–30 minute nap)
4–6 months	• Introduce solids • 4 breastfeeds a day	• start with beginner foods between 4–6 months; check with your doctor (see page 36 for more info)
6 months or after	• Introduce vegetables, fruits, meats, other proteins • 3 breastfeeds a day: when baby awakens, before afternoon nap, before night sleep	• everything pureed • follow your doctor's advice if he advises differently (see page 36 for more info)
8 months	• Baby can try pureed food with some lumps • 3 breastfeeds a day (when awakens, before afternoon nap, before night sleep)	• can start pureeing family dinners, with added liquid (see page 36 for more info)

The Schedule
Expanded

Newborn Stage

Feeding every 3 hours

When the baby is first born, the immediate goal is to get the mom's milk flowing. At this stage, Julia advises to feed the baby both breasts every 3 hours and not to let the baby go longer than 3 hours without feeding.

Julia states that it is important for the baby to get the colostrom every 3 hours during the day in the beginning. Therefore, most mothers should encourage feeding every 3 hours so that the milk supply is produced sooner rather than later. Still, if baby goes longer during the night, let him sleep. Then when the milk does come in, the breasts are so full that they need to be emptied in order to prevent an infection or blocked duct. Feeding every 3 hours during the day will help avoid these problems. When the milk supply is more established, usually by the end of the first week, the feeds can slowly start to be stretched to 4 hours apart. This may take a long time, even weeks. You can't rush or force the baby.

With Julia's ninth baby, she was sleeping 5 hours—or more if she didn't waken the baby—during the day. Her mother said not to let the baby go that long without feeding so as to increase Julia's milk supply. At this point, feeding every 5 hours may actually discourage milk production. Then it would take her longer to establish the night stretch because the baby would require more milk to make up the total calorie consumption needed in a 24 hr span. That being said, still let baby go longer during the night, but keep the day feedings to every 3 or 4 hours.

Remember this essential key to success: feed the baby on both sides. Julia advises not to let the feed go longer than 20 minutes on each side as this is exhausting for the baby. As well, they start to change their reason for nursing, to think of it not for feeding, but for 'suck and sleep.' The goal is to create good feeding habits.

When the baby starts to make her first little fussing noises, do not be too anxious to feed the baby right away. To stop a baby crying, the most obvious answer is to breastfeed. But this is not always what the baby needs. Just listen to her for a few moments. Our bedroom is next to the baby's room and we leave both doors ajar. When the baby first cries, I lay there and pray that she goes back to sleep. Often she will! So stay out of sight—if she sees you, she may get even more upset and demand to feed. She may just be making noises in her sleep—some babies are really noisy—or she may wake for a moment and fall asleep again. She may need a burp or a diaper change. Or she may be cold if her blankets have fallen off. You may be able to remedy the situation by doing one or more of the following: burping, changing the diaper, or putting on a blanket without feeding. But first of all, get in the habit of waiting to determine her true needs. Julia advises letting the baby wait three minutes the first time. Then five minutes. The next night, you may allow the baby to wait ten to fifteen minutes.

Some moms may have the wherewithal to let their babies cry. If you are this type of mom, make sure you check on your baby if she has been crying persistently for any length of time, such as 10 minutes.

Remember, some babies are quick feeders and some are extremely slow. Despite all the adjustments or hiccups along the way, it is a great time to put your feet up with a glass of water and a good book and to relax and bond with baby.

Is your baby feeding less than 3 hours apart at this point? See page 21 for ideas on how to stretch the time in between the baby's feeds.

Does your baby have her nights and days turned around? See the Troubleshooting section on page 42.

So, now you've got the baby feeding every 3 hours apart, or you are working on it. Remember that very important piece of advice from Julia: if the baby is sleeping in the night, let her sleep!

4 or 5 Days Old

a) Stretching the feeds to 4 hours

How we are created really helps us here—by four days or so, you should be engorged and have plenty of milk for full feeds on both sides. You should have enough to provide the baby with a meal (not just a snack as before the milk came in) and she will be more satisfied and therefore comfortable between feedings.

Now that the milk has come in, you can work on stretching the feeds, little by little, so that you are feeding the baby every 4 hours. For example, you feed at 6:00 am, then 10:00 am, then 2:00 pm, then 6:00 pm, 10:00 pm, 2:00 am etc. This can be achieved by week two. Always remember—there is no need to rush the baby. Just keep working on it without stopping. My daughters like to quote the fable of the tortoise and the hare, "Slow and steady wins the race."

This goal may seem unrealistic if your baby was born feeding every hour. In fact, one of ours was like that. Take your baby's natural schedule as the starting point, whatever that is. If she feeds every hour, then add 15 minutes. So now you would be feeding after 1 hour and 15 minutes. Then, at the next feed, wait 1 hour and 30 minutes. Keep adding those extra minutes so that she is feeding every 2 hours, then slowly build up to every 3 hours, and so on until you reach 4 hours. Most likely it will not go perfectly smoothly, but that is life with a baby. Just accept where you are, do not give up and keep on trying! Remember, this is a schedule tailored to you and your baby. The goal is to teach your baby to develop good feeding routines.

So, how exactly is it possible to get the baby to 'wait'? After all, patience is not a virtue all babies are born with. Turn to page 21 for a list of ways to extend time between feedings. If you are still at a loss as to how to begin, start doing each item on the list one by one. Fifteen minutes will be up before you know it!

If you are blessed with a lot of milk, you may be uncomfortably engorged. In this case, use warm wash clothes on your breast before you feed as it helps the milk to flow. You can also pump after you feed to empty the breast until your body adjusts to producing the amount your baby needs. As Julia says, it is amazing how our breasts will adjust to the baby's demands.

b) **20 minutes awake time** before bed

Start a bedtime tradition of spending **20 minutes of 'quality time'** before giving the baby his last feed and jumping into bed yourself. In other words, calculate when you would like to give the baby his last feed. Then make sure your baby is awake for 20 minutes before this feed. Refer to page 21 for ideas on how to spend those minutes. Julia likes to use this time to bathe the baby, most days just with water so as not to dry out the baby's skin. This establishes a routine. Babies thrive on regularity. It makes them feel secure.

After 20 minutes is up, now is the time to **feed the baby**. Relax with her and make sure she has fed a full feed on both sides if possible. If she is falling asleep, you can wake her by taking off some of her clothes, changing her diaper or using a damp/wet face cloth gently on her skin. This is the advice my doctor gave me with my first newborn as a touch of jaundice made her sleepy. Afterwards, give the baby a *really* good burp. A good burp is essential! See pages 32–36 for advice on burping.

Then **wrap the baby tightly**. "Like a womb," as Julia says. She always encourages moms to swaddle their babies. Try to make sure his sheets are tucked around him tightly, so he is cozy. A bassinette or cradle helps.

Julia highly recommends the baby learning to fall asleep on his own. Julia turns on a teddy that plays music which signals to baby that it is time to sleep. With the baby, she says prayers, kisses, sings to baby, and then leaves the room, closing the door. She doesn't use soothers or leave lights on. She also does not rock the baby to sleep, while acknowledging that occasionally this may happen, as long as it is not the norm. The idea is to help the baby depend upon the routine, not other things, for comfort and security.

Now is the moment you have been waiting for—take advantage of it and **jump into bed**! Avoid the temptation to do housework or chores. Your sleep is more important. And, again—do not wake the baby during the night.

One Week Old

a) Continue to work on **stretching the feeds to every 4 hours**

At this stage, feeding the baby more than 4 hours apart may back fire. As Julia explains, if the feeds are too far apart, for example every 5 hours, it would take longer to establish the night stretch because the baby would require more milk to make up the total required calorie consumption in a 24-hour span. So, feed every 4 hours during the day for the first 3–4 weeks, while working on lengthening the night stretch. Then you can stretch up to 5 hours (by 2 months) during the day if the baby is sleeping at least 8.5 hours at night. Let the baby go longer during the night at any time if they want.

b) **Increase the awake time before the last feed** little by little so that the baby is awake for about 20–30 minutes before the last feed AND

c) **Push the middle of the night feed later**

Make sure the baby is feeding at least every 4 hours during the day before pushing the middle of the night feed later. Once this is established, it's time for this exciting stage (exciting because soon everyone will be sleeping more!)

Concentrate on the period before the last feed. Keep the baby awake more during this time. In fact, this should be her prime awake time every day. If the baby is only a week old, she probably won't be awake for more than 25–45 minutes. Every week, this time will increase.

When the baby wakes up for his accustomed feed (whether it is 1:00 am or 3:00 am, etc.), do not pick him up right away. Let him wait for maybe 3 minutes, and then during the next night 5 minutes, and on the following night 10 minutes, and so on. This will help him not to become demanding. Often he will whimper a little, talk a bit and sometimes even fall back asleep.

While in this stage of eliminating the middle of night feed, you may have to be flexible with feeding times during the day. In the morning, make a plan around when you would like to feed the baby that day. You will have to base it on the first feed of the day and that time may be changing every day for a while. The baby is used to waiting a set number of hours before she feeds, so stick to not feeding her before she expects it. If you feed her sooner than she expects, she will get used to having smaller amounts of food more often and will be waking more during the night.

After One Month Old

a) Baby can **sleep through the night (6–7 hours** straight)

   If the baby is feeding every four hours throughout the day, she should be sleeping a good 6 hours at night. But, of course, if the baby wants to sleep longer, let her!

b) Keep working at **stretching the feeds to every 4 hours**

If the baby is not yet sleeping a good stretch at night and you have not stretched the feeds to 4 hours apart during the day, keep on working at it. Do not move ahead until this is done. There is no big rush. If you are persistent, it will happen!

c) Continue with the **45 minutes of awake time before the last feed**

Also, keep in mind that around this time, babies will often go through another growth spurt (see page 40). Because the baby is growing more, he may want to feed more. There is no need to push things, so, if necessary, give the baby an extra feed in between the scheduled feeds. That will give him some extra time to adjust. When you do this, keep the scheduled feeds as full feeds—always from both sides—with the extra feed being a smaller feed in-between.

2–2.5 Months Old

a) Baby should be **sleeping about 8 hours** straight

Once the baby has reached the 8 hour mark, you can start adjusting her bedtime so that she is going to sleep earlier in the evening. Julia believes that at this stage it is better to have babies sleeping longer hours before midnight rather than sleeping longer in the morning. It not only helps them in their current stage, but will help ease them into more of a set pattern of morning and afternoon naps.

Julia gives the following example of how to adjust the baby's bedtime:

Say the last feed was 10:30 pm, bring the feed down to 10:00. Once baby has mastered that and is still waking at her normal time, say 6:00 or 6:30 am, give her next night feed at 9:30 pm. When the baby has adjusted to the new time of waking at 6:30 am, then bring her night feed down to 9:00 pm. After the other kids are down (say 8:30 pm), then it is baby's feeding time.

Following the above example, the baby's feeds would look like this: 6:30 am feed, 10:00 am feed, 2:00 pm feed, 6:00 pm feed, 9:00 pm feed. Note that there are only 4 hours before the last feed at this point. Do not provide fewer than 4 good feeds a day.

b) Start **stretching the feeds to every 5 hours**

Once the routine of feeding 4 hours apart and sleeping 8 hours at night is firmly established, it is time to start working on the 5 hour stretch. This will help extend the night time sleep. See page 21 for ideas on how to stretch the time between feeds.

Before doing this, make sure of two things: 1) your breasts are producing enough milk and 2) the baby is on track with his weight gain and that acid reflux, allergies or other medical issues are not presenting a problem. Be sure to check his weight gain and general health with your doctor.

c) Baby's **awake time before her last feed has increased to the whole 5 hours**, except for a 20–30 minute nap.

Stretching Out
Baby's Feeds

Stretching the times between the feeds is **key** to successfully helping the baby develop a regular sleep schedule.

As soon as the baby is born, she will often be feeding on a 'schedule' of her own making right off the bat. Our fourth was feeding every 3 hours right away. Our third started off wanting to feed every hour, especially through the night. Whatever your baby is doing, start by paying attention to how often the baby is feeding. Writing it down really helps. (See page 51 for a sample feed tracking chart.) Keep in mind that if the baby is getting a good feed on both breasts, she should not be hungry before two hours.

Then, on about the fourth or fifth day, when your milk is in and the baby has got the hang of feeding, start slowly stretching the feeds to every 4 hours. Four hours is the goal and this goal will not be achieved right away, but only by working at it little by little. This goal is often achieved by distracting the baby for a short time before his next feed.

Ideas to Distract Baby for Those Extra Minutes

- walk around the house with the baby—in circles if necessary—or go for a walk outside—or better yet, have someone else do it.

- gently bounce the baby while sitting or walking. Babies tend not to want their mom to sit down, so resign yourself early on to walking a lot.

- hold the baby securely, especially supporting the neck, and swing her while walking. Try different speeds to see what she would like.

- put baby in an age-appropriate swing chair

- change his diaper and make it fun by talking to the baby, massaging him and taking longer than usual

- while walking, change baby's position—e.g. put her on your shoulder, next lying in your arms, next hold her in front of you

- let him exercise his lungs a bit

- put her in a baby Bjorn or something similar and walk around the house cleaning up the older kids toys/ folding laundry, and so on

- distract baby with toys

- interact with baby while talking and smiling

- put baby on her tummy, encouraging her

- walk around with him and pat his bottom. This reminds him of the heart beat of mom in utero.

- if it is before the last feed, bathe the baby and stretch the time for bathing. One of my girls enjoyed the bath when she was newborn—she would be happy for 15 minutes having water splashed on her.

- get older siblings and dad to help with the distracting if possible

Trying the suggested distractions can really add minutes to the time between feeds. Changing a diaper can take 5 minutes on its own!

If stretching a feed another 15 minutes seems too long, aim for 10 minutes. The point is to keep stretching the feeds. Every little bit helps.

Awake Time
Before Last Feed

You will see in The Schedule that Julia gives her babies a certain amount of 'awake time' before the very last feed. Along with stretching the feeds, the awake time is the second part of helping the baby order his entire day.

When a baby's awake time is longest before the last feed, his overall awake time will naturally expand downwards into the day. With my last 5 babies, the same pattern emerged with all of them. First their awake time would be almost only at night before the last feed, then a bit more in the mid-afternoon, then a bit more in early afternoon, and so on.

Julia says the awake time before the last feed is simply an amount of time that the baby is awake immediately before his last feed. As stated in The Schedule, the approximate times are:

Age	Minutes awake
4–5 days	10–20 minutes*
1 week	20–30 minutes*
1 month	45–60 minutes*
2–2.5 months	entire time since previous feed (may have 15–20 minute nap)

* includes bath time

If the baby is only a week old, she will not be awake for more then 20 minutes plus bath time. Each week this awake time increases. By 11 weeks or so, she is awake the whole five hours. During awake time, play with her, massage her, put her in a rocking chair, let her play with rattles. Father and older siblings can help out here, too. Baby may also have a little cry during this time.

If baby has a good awake time, and a good bath, then the baby is really hungry and tired and feeds very well. Through this routine, the baby's sleep will lengthen up to 5 hours quickly and longer. Having the baby fall asleep in his own bed, as opposed to any place or in someone's arms, helps the baby to be secure in his surroundings since he remembers where he fell asleep and is not startled or disoriented. There is a higher chance that the baby will fall back asleep. If the baby does wake in the night do not pick him up right away, but let him wait a couple of minutes at first. Then each night after that, wait a little longer.

Having this practice of not immediately picking the baby up helps the baby to be patient and not panic if Mom is not there immediately. Often he will fall back asleep. When the baby is picked up with the intention of feeding him, take a good 15 minutes changing his diaper, talking to him, getting yourself a big glass of water, walking around, and so on. Then feed. You have to put that effort in. It will pay off soon—better sooner than a lot later!

Soon baby will feed at 10:00 or 11:00 pm at night and last until 5:00 am. The night stretch will gradually increase to 6:00 am. Once the wake time is regular and is at a time that suits the family (6:00 am or even 7:00 am), then you can start to begin the night feed routine earlier. Often, the ideal last feed for the baby is around 8:30 pm, once older siblings are in bed. To start the last feed earlier, go by half hour increments.

If you are feeding at 10:00 pm, try a 9:30 pm feed, keeping the ideal morning feed at the same time. Once this is consistent, then go to a 9:00 pm feed, then 8:30 pm. By a month, baby can be sleeping 6–7 hours. At the second month mark, the nights could lengthen very quickly, even within a week, and a five hour stretch can be reached during the day. An example of a feeding schedule is: 6:00 am, 11:00 am, 4:00 pm and 8:30 pm.

The reason for the night stretch lengthening quickly after the second month is because the baby:

- is stretching the day feed to be 4–5 hours between feeds

- is retaining more milk and

- has the proper day routine and night preparation, including awake time before the last feed

This combination of factors very naturally leads to successfully lengthened night time sleeps.

Typical
Sleep Schedule

Every new mom wonders why she is so exhausted while her baby is sleeping so much! How much should baby actually be sleeping? Based on her experience, Julia has come up with some guidelines. Remember, they are just general guidelines.

Newborns—6–18 hours total

- 5 hours through the night, feeding every 3 hours

- note: since your milk is still coming in, the baby's feeds might be a little shorter

Newborns (one week plus)—16–18 hours total

- awake time = feeding time

- feed every 4 hours, 6 feeds in 24 hours (40 minute feeding + burping time = 1 hour)

- routine of feed/ burp/ awake time started

One month old—14–16 hours total

- sleeping 6–8 hrs at night

- typical schedule:

- 6:00 am wake, feed

- 7:00 am sleep

- 10:00 am wake, feed, awake time

- 12:00 noon sleep

- 2:00 pm wake, feed

- 3:30 sleep

- 6:00 pm feed, awake time, 20 min nap, more awake time

- 9:30 pm last feed

2 months old—14–16 total

- sleeping 8 hours + at night

- naps—morning, afternoon, short evening nap

6 months old—14–15 total

- sleeping 8 hours or more at night

- naps—morning, afternoon (longer than before as baby drops her evening nap)

12 months old—13–15 total

- sleeping 11 hours or more at night

- naps—morning (1 hour), afternoon (1.5–2.5 hours)

18 months–3 years—12–15 hours total

- 11–12 hours at night

- afternoon nap is between 1.5–3 hours long (depending on their bedtime)

- Julia keeps the nap to 2 hours, 8:00–9:00 pm bedtime, 6:00–7:00 am wake time

Troubleshooting

Your baby has a message for you and he is giving you a clue. When he changes his routine, think of it that way. The clue is the change of routine and will lead you to the message, which is the underlying reason. For example, the baby may be teething or he has not been burped enough before he sleeps.... Whatever it is, we just need to follow the clues, dig a bit deeper and find out what the baby is trying to tell us!

Acid Reflux

Acid reflux occurs when the stomach contents come back up, causing the baby to gag, choke or spit up. Our little son had acid reflux. His symptoms included coughing, producing lots of mucus, wheezy breathing, pulling off when feeding, gagging on his milk in his sleep and lots of spitting up. We took him to a pediatrician who told us that every baby has acid reflux to a greater or lesser degree. Our little guy did not have it to an extreme degree, but it affected him far more than any of our girls. These are the practical tips the pediatrician gave us:

- raise the bed mattress to be sloping downwards slightly. You can wedge them in with a towel behind their back so that they cannot roll over.

- when feeding the baby, keep him as upright as possible, with his head up and his body going down into your lap, between your legs. This is easier for digestion.

- during feeding, burp the baby between sides and any time it seems necessary

- keep the baby upright for at least 20–30 minutes after feeding

- the best burping position is with the baby's stomach on the collar bone. This may be higher than you are used to.

- after feeding, the best position for the baby is on his tummy on a hard cushion that is sloped upwards, with the head at the highest point, since the pressure on his tummy is soothing. Make sure to watch the baby for rolling.

- try not to put the baby in his car seat for at least a half hour after feeding since the car seat puts the baby into a crunch position and is uncomfortable for him

Julia had some experience with acid reflux with one of her babies. Below she shares her insights on this topic:

I could tell the baby had discomfort because he had these symptoms of irritability—pulling off a lot when feeding and losing the proper latch, lots of spitting up, general crankiness, wheezy breathing, cranky periods after a feed, and not gaining enough weight.

When the baby was three weeks old, I realized things were not normal with him. I had to stop everything and simplify my life to concentrate solely on the baby for a while. I even had to help him to relearn to latch properly. When breastfeeding, **check the baby's latch**. I found that my baby would lose the good latch as the reflux made him uncomfortable, thereby not stimulating my supply of milk. Also, make sure you **feed both sides**, (even if it is ten minutes and seven minutes). If you are still quite full, then pump the excess to avoid breast infections. Somehow your body adjusts to the demand soon enough. When switching sides, always try to bring up a burp. This minimizes big spit ups.

He would have really cranky periods after his feeds. My husband figured out that **placing the baby's tummy on his shoulder** really soothed the baby.

As far as feeding the baby, I stuck to every 4 hours and did not think about pushing it to 5 because he wasn't gaining weight. Acid reflux is tricky, because the baby doesn't breast feed well, as he is uncomfortable when feeding. The discomfort leads to lessened consumption, and in turn, lessened milk production. It is hard to tell how much baby is getting and you may have to feed more often (maybe every 3 hours even). Despite this, I found he would still sleep through the night 6–8 hours.

By three months, I had to stop breast feeding because I couldn't tell if he was getting enough breast milk and his weight was in the lower tenth percentile. So I fed him formula.

At five months, we **saw a pediatrician** as we thought the wheezy breathing indicated asthma. The pediatrician said it was not asthma, but the acid reflux causing the lungs to produce mucus—thereby creating a wheezy sound. The pediatrician started us on a special easily-digestible formula to increase weight gain and then two types of medication to de-acidify the stomach and increase stomach absorption. It was a real challenge with all the timing of the meds and feeds. I still stuck to feeding every 4 hours.

Around six months, we started him on rice cereal and kept to this for a little while. As soon as he hit a year, his weight improved and we tried weaning him off the meds, and he has never stopped eating! Now he is a very tall kid. At five years of age, he wore a size six. He eats double servings at breakfast, lunch and dinner. But as a baby, I was never able to feed him more than five or six ounces of milk at a time. With my other kids I would fill the bottle to eight ounces.

Even though our baby had this acid reflux he was still able to sleep through the night (even if he was small). I highly suggest a sloped bed and a soft blanky so baby can self-soothe and suck a couple of fingers! They fall asleep so willingly.

Breastfeeding

Positioning of baby and mom

Sit fairly upright in a comfortable chair, preferably with arms. Have your legs with your feet flat on the floor and your thighs parallel to the ground (use a footstool if necessary). Place a fluffy pillow or good breast feed cushion on your lap. The baby should be able to lie on this pillow and comfortably feed from your breast.

If feeding in the cradle position, cup the back of the baby's head with the hand on the side the baby is not feeding on. Make sure your thumb and fingers are straight up and down with your hand and not on the baby's cheeks. If fingers are on the cheeks, you may inadvertently press on the cheek muscles and make it harder for the baby to feed.

With your other hand, hold your breast as though you were holding a hamburger. When the baby's mouth opens wide, bring the breast towards her, aiming the nipple towards the top of the baby's mouth. You are aiming to get a large amount of the breast in her mouth. Make sure the baby's tongue is down and preferably stretched forward.

Also important is the positioning of the bottom lip. Make sure it is relaxed and pulled out and down, exposing the inside of the lip. You may need to use the pointer finger that is holding your breast to pull his chin and/ or lip down for a good latch.

If the latch is not a good one, break the seal by placing your finger in the baby's mouth and gently opening it a bit. Keep working at it until the latch is good.

The above is excellent advice I learned from a doctor specializing in breastfeeding.

Julia also suggests having a big glass of water as you are feeding the baby, and making sure the baby empties both breasts so that the baby gets both front and hind milk.

Burping

Getting those air bubbles to come up is extremely important for a lot of babies. Interestingly, my first and fourth didn't need to be burped half as much as the others.

A doctor once explained to me the rationale behind burping. Burps are simply bubbles of air. The baby's body needs to be moved to allow that bubble to come to the surface. Lying her down for a minute allows the air bubble to move around a bit and then when you sit her up, it may just pop right out.

When you are breastfeeding and have finished the first side, spend a few minutes to bring up a burp. Often a small burp will come up quickly. Then feed the second side. When the feeding is done, spend a longer time burping the baby.

What happens if you do not burp a baby? There are a number of answers:

1. Nothing. Some babies are not bothered by those air bubbles. However, beware, because most of them are, to some extent.

2. Nothing... initially. Say you try to burp the baby and nothing happens. So you lay the baby down thinking she may just not need to burp—and besides, you are exhausted. You flop into bed, but an hour or two later, when it is not her normal time to waken, the baby is up screaming. This was happening to me with my second baby. I would burp her for ten minutes and nothing would happen, so I gave up and put her in bed and, yes, she would be up screaming and I could not console her. She did not even want to feed—or if she did, feeding made it worse. When I asked my doctor she said that because the air bubble wasn't brought up right away, it goes further into the intestines and has to come out the other way. This is a longer and more painful process for the baby whose insides are not fully developed. After that, I would burp her as long as it took—even 45 minutes. It was worth it, because after that she would not be bothered by the gas. A common mistake would be to try to feed the baby right away (before the baby is 'due'). The baby will then have to be burped anyway. This is a vicious cycle. Put the time in to bring up the burp the first time.

3. She throws up—a lot! A rogue bubble will sometimes force its way up to the surface bringing with it the baby's recent meal.

4. She cries and cries until the bubble comes out on its own.

Clearly helping the baby to burp is the best option.

Burping Positions

Below are some ideas on different positions to try when burping the baby. Each baby is different and some positions may work better than others. So, experiment for a while until you have found what works.

The two main ideas for an effective burp are:

1. **Put pressure on the tummy**. Some pressure is necessary, but you will have to figure out how much is good for your particular baby. Some need a lot in order to burp, others need next to nothing and if they get too much, will empty their tummy completely.

2. **Don't block the air flow from tummy to mouth**. Make sure the baby's spine is straight.

The Positions

1. Baby is sitting on your lap, with your hand supporting her chin and jaw line and with her outside cheek resting on your fingers. The baby is slightly bent forward. Your other hand is alternating patting and stroking upwards with pressure. Keep an eye on the baby's posture. Make sure she a) is leaning forward enough so there is pressure on her tummy, and b) has a straight spine. If she is slouching, the air bubble may stay trapped inside.

2. Baby is upright, against your chest looking over your shoulder. With a strong hand pat the baby's back.

3. Baby is sitting on your lap facing you, lying back. Your left hand is supporting her top back and neck and your right hand is patting her back. This position is not as effective but sometimes the change of

position is good and it does not put pressure on the full stomach. This position is also good if you have a spitty baby.

4. When the burp is not coming up, lie baby across your lap level, face up, with your right hand behind the baby's neck, base of head and top of back. Then sit them up fairly quickly. Sometimes an air bubble is stuck and will dislodge with the sudden movement.

5. Have the baby facing you on one of your shoulders. Position the baby's tummy on your collar bone, so she is quite high up. Pat or stroke the baby's back. However, be warned—if you have an extremely spitty baby, this extra pressure may cause a bit of an explosion! Depending on the baby, you may want to wait a few hours after feeding to do this position. On the other hand, if your baby does not often spit up, this may be the position that works best for her.

6. If the baby is disturbed by a bubble an hour or more after feeding, lie baby face down across your thighs. Sit down on a bed or the floor with your legs straight in front of you, with one knee slightly bent. The baby's head is over your top thigh and her body is lying across your lower thigh. Rub upwards on the baby's back or lightly pat her.

Both Julia and a doctor that I spoke to recommend trying to burp the baby after feeding him on the first side before feeding the second breast. Often a small burp will come up quite quickly. Then move on to feeding the second side and afterwards spend a longer time getting all those bubbles up.

Julia also recommends the baby's bed be raised at the head by placing a couple of towels under the head of the mattress. This, she says, helps with both bubbles and digestion. The slope will help the bubble float up and out and gravity will help the digestion process.

One caveat on placing towels under the mattress—do not make it too high or you may find the baby has rolled to the end of the crib.

Feeding Solids

These days solids are introduced somewhere between four to six months. Again, this is highly subjective, but some rough guidelines are often helpful. Here Julia outlines six steps in introducing food to your toddler. Introduce each new step little by little. For example, start with only feeding the baby cereal at 7:30 am after the 6:00 am breastfeed. Once she is taking a substantial amount, go on to step two, adding in another solid food feeding at 6:00 pm.

Some doctors will advise introducing each new food to the baby by giving her one teaspoon for three days in a row to see if the baby has any adverse reaction to the food. Recently, however, a pediatrician advised me not to do this. He also said to introduce meat first and never to give the baby rice cereal. There is a lot of advice out there. The bottom line is to use your common sense and if you have any health concerns or major allergies in your family to check with your doctor.

To begin, start the baby with just a few teaspoons of cereal or other food recommended by your doctor. Make the consistency not too thick so that it is easier for the baby to swallow. The aim is to get the baby used to the food and the spoon in her mouth and to learn what to do with the food. Each day you add more cereal. Keep the regular breast feed going (four feeds a day). After a couple of weeks, the baby is now eating a good size meal.

Please keep in mind that these times are just suggestions. Times can vary by half an hour or more. You should base your schedule on what is best for baby, parents and siblings.

Steps for starting solids (keeping the regular four breastfeeds a day 6am/10am/4pm/8pm):

1st	7:30 am cereal
2nd	6:00 pm cereal
3rd	1:00 pm veggies
4th	1:00 pm veggies **and** meat fruit dessert/yogurt
5th	after afternoon sleep (3:30-ish) either breastfeed (if you still do four feeds) or give a snack such as apple, juice, mum mums, baby cookie
6th	can substitute pureed dinners for baby's cereal. Add water or chicken broth to pureed family dinner to make food softer for the baby. Then you can increase the amount of lumps as his teeth come in and he seems able to tolerate the lumpiness.

So, incorporating only the first step, the baby's day would look like this:

6:00 am	breastfeed
7:30 am	cereal
11:30 am	breastfeed
4:00 pm	breastfeed
8:30 pm	breastfeed

After all six steps are incorporated, you can think about cutting out one breast feed. Bringing the 1:00 pm solid feed time to earlier in the day, the baby's schedule would then look like this:

6:00 am	breastfeed
7:30 am	cereal
11:00 am	veggies and meat, water/juice
1:15-ish	breastfeed
3:30–4:00 pm	snack (e.g. juice/water, mum mums or baby cookie etc)
5:30 pm	cereal, ¼–½ mashed banana or pureed family dinner
8:00–8:30 pm	breastfeed

Remember to give the baby water to drink with his meals and snacks. The above schedule will most likely work until you decide to wean the baby off of breast milk.

As the baby grows, the amounts of food and the food texture changes. By nine months you should be able to puree your dinners for the baby. By 12 months, the baby may be having Cheerios, Weetabix, oatmeal, and so on. Also, at breakfast, the baby can always have a piece of toast with Australian Vegemite. Julia's children love it.

Please remember throughout this entire book that the goal is to modify it to suit your family's needs. For example, when my son started eating solids, the first feed that I added was around 5:00 or 6:00 pm. The main reason for this was so that one of the older girls could help me out by feeding him. Eventually, I added the morning cereal feed.

Another tip: when feeding the baby food, let him hold a spoon as well, so he can get the feel of the spoon. This helps him by developing coordination as well as distracting the baby from intercepting your spoon and making a mess. Remember, this is not 100% effective. It helps the baby get used to feeding himself by about a year. A pediatrician I know advocates the baby self-feeding as soon as possible. He even said to give the baby a bowl with a spoon or even to just play with the food until he realizes that he can put it in his own mouth. This will help him to be more self-suffi-cient and therefore less picky in his food choices when older. Note that it will be a little messy for a while, but it is good for the baby's independence and if you have a number of children you can more easily tend to them all.

Gassy Babies

Some babies are gassier than others. I have had a wide spectrum of gassy versus non gassy babies among my children. Julia explains that babies sometimes like pressure on their tummy by carrying them with their stomach resting high on your collar blade. Another position that can be soothing to their stomach is placing the baby face down on your forearm, with her head in the crook of your arm and her stomach on your hand. Gently patting her back with your free hand can help further calm her stomach.

Growth Spurts

When and if growth spurts happen is a matter of debate. And, if they do occur fairly regularly as some assert, whether they actually affect the baby is another matter. It is comparable to teething. With some babies, the teeth pop out without anyone noticing. With other babies, each tooth is preceded by months of screaming. The same kind of thing can happen with growth spurts. In other words, you may or may not notice them.

In Julia's experience with babies, she found they would typically grow quickly at the following times:

ten days

three weeks

six weeks

three months

six months

These are rough estimates and may be out by either days or weeks. Again, each baby is different.

At these times, the feeding schedule may differ. Julia will often fit in an extra feed for the baby or bring the feedings closer together.

Mastitis

Julia's sister suffered from frequent mastitis which made it impossible to do Julia's exact method. She would get mastitis if she went longer than 3 hours between feeds. She shared with me how she dealt with this while helping the babies to remain on a regular schedule:

What I do is quite simple. I feed them about every three hours during the day. Actually, I do not mind perhaps once a day feeding under the three hour mark: often just before going to bed at night to top them off. Then I feed them during the night as they wake …usually three to five hours in the first couple of weeks and then it stretches a little to six hours by about five weeks. Then mysteriously anywhere between the 8 to 13 week mark the baby just does not wake at night anymore and sleeps straight through for 11 to 13 hours. I have no idea why but so far it happened for all 4 of mine. Once they sleep through the night, I might have to pump in the middle of the night for one or two weeks until the supply of milk adjusts to fewer feeds, thus preventing mastitis. I continue the three hour feeds in the day if the baby wants to but as they get older often it will stretch a little longer (sometimes four hours). For the most part, though, it tends to stay around the three hour mark. Once they are on solid food then I feed them upon waking, before their morning sleep, before their afternoon sleep and at night.

Nocturnal Babies

After her 9th baby, Julia learned something new—that some babies really do have their internal clocks reversed! Here are her own words:

> I never believed that there was a baby whose routine you could not sort out by working on the daily regular feeding of 4 hours and by preparing their evenings by keeping them more alert, stimulated, bathed and fed, all resulting in a longer night's sleep.
>
> My ninth baby proved me wrong! She was really nocturnal—dead to the world during the day and awake and cranky during the nights! It took me two weary-eyed months to work with her and set her clock right. I was so exhausted that I even felt my mind was detached from my body, floating somewhere else.
>
> Be patient. Eventually you will get there. During the day at hour four, when it was my baby's time to feed, she was completely uninterested. I tried everything to wake her—taking off her clothes, putting cold wet cloths on her—desperate measures. She still would not wake to feed. It was so tempting to let her continue to sleep—I needed the sleep, too, plus there were the other kids to tend to. I knew if I gave in to **not** putting the effort in to wake her and feed her, the whole routine/schedule would never be set and I would be a wreck and my whole family would suffer too.
>
> Try to stick to the plan, day after day. Each baby is different. I cannot predict when each baby will get it. It took me two long months. Keep trying. Now she is 15 months and has slept through the night since two

months old, but compared to my other children, she really does not seem to need as much sleep.

Have perseverance! Yes, two months is long when you are in it, but it is only two months. That is nothing compared to some babies who are in the habit of sleeping poorly for many years. It is worth all the effort.

Nursing to Sleep—Older Babies

One mom I know had an eight month-old who would only go to sleep for naps and at night if she was nursed. She did not take a bottle or soother. Julia's advice was to write down her feeding and napping times on paper to see the timing. Then she could make adjustments to these so that the baby has a set routine. An example of a schedule could be:

6:30 am	**wake and breast feed**
7:30 am	**cereal and ½ toast with jam**
9:30 am	**water and ½ apple juice**
10:00 am	**nap**
11:00 am	**veggies/meat**
1:00 pm	**breastfeed or snack**
——— afternoon nap ———	
6:00 pm	**dinner**
8:00 pm	**breastfeed**

For the naps, set a routine that the baby will get used to. Remember the importance of the baby having his own room or sleeping space.

Morning nap—Turn off any lights, tone down your voice, give cuddles, and tell the baby that it is sleepy time. Sing a lullaby and play sleepy music, perhaps using a teddy with pull cord, and cozily tuck baby into the crib. A bunny or soft blankie is helpful to soothe them. Kiss and calmly stroke her and say good night. Go quietly and calmly out of the room and close the door smoothly. If she is upset, let her cry for perhaps five minutes at first, then go in and restart the calming routine. Pick her up and cuddle all over again, just to confirm it is alright. It does not have to take long; a few minutes is good. If she cries again, let her go for ten minutes. Often she will figure it out and go to sleep. It is true that sometimes there are personalities who are more difficult to soothe. This is where a soft blankie or bunny can be a wonderful help.

Afternoon nap—After ten months, Julia will give the baby a bottle on the couch, laying her down with her bunny and tucked in cozily. After she is finished, she takes her upstairs and puts her in bed with the same song as in the morning nap if she needs it, making the blankets nice and tight, kissing her and leaving the room. She does not put the baby to sleep with a bottle in order to prevent cavities.

Night bedtime—By this age, the baby probably will not be taking a nap after dinner. She can read, play, have her bath, breast feed and brush her teeth if she has any. Then, as in the morning nap, do the same routine of cuddling/rocking, singing, tucking into bed with cozy blankets, prayers, kisses and reassuring words such as "It's time for sleep, Honey, sweet dreams" and so on. Babies are smart. We often underestimate them and think they will not understand, but they do. They especially understand our tone of voice. Reassuring is very important.

Older Babies—Just Starting the Schedule

Not everyone can start this 'schedule' when the baby is a newborn. It often happens that a baby is almost not a baby anymore and is still not sleeping through the night. In fact, it happened to me.

In this case, the first thing Julia asks is if the baby is sleeping in the parent's bed. This first step is crucial. The little one needs to develop a sense of independence, to learn to be secure in his own bed and to feel safe in the knowledge that mom and dad are close by, even if they are in a different room.

After this step, you can move to working on the middle of the night feeds. When the baby wakes, talk to him, tell him there is no feeding at night. Say, "Mommy loves you," kiss him, "night, night" and close the door.

This may happen a few times. The third time, take the baby to the sink and give him a drink of water. Put him down, reassuring him that everything is alright.

The "put down routine" is very important—sing to the baby, pull his cord stuffy toy, tuck him in cozily, talk calmly to him. You may have to let him cry. You know that he is no longer thirsty. If his crying persists more than ten minutes the first time, go back to him, explain that mommy does not feed in the night anymore. Offer him water again. The next time, let the baby go fifteen minutes, then offer water again. Put him down once more. In Julia's experience, this pattern has been effective.

A different idea is to wean the baby off of breast milk by a year. Before bed, give her eight ounces of 3% milk. Then brush her teeth since the milk may cause cavities. It is a matter of breaking the habit of the baby waking for a comfort feed. Julia's method is about making feed times meal times, not comfort times. We have comfort time with our baby through cuddling, playing, kissing, and other interaction.

Put Down Routine for Naps and Nighttime

The following is a repetition of some advice from the previous two sections. This is a deliberate repetition since the put down routine is key to helping your baby feel comfortable and secure enough to drift off to sleep. It therefore deserves a section all to itself!

As you can see in many areas of a babies' life, they love a routine. So a consistent put down routine will help them whenever it is time to sleep. It does not have to be too rigid or long. In fact, it may not be helpful to either you or the baby if it takes too long. I heard of one mom who would rock the baby to sleep for a long time, then very gingerly put her down, sliding her arm out from under the baby super slowly. Then the mom would slide down to the floor and slowly crawl backwards towards the door to leave the room. This process was very rigid and took a long time. Our aim here is to have the nap be firstly, decided on by Mom and secondly, agreed to by baby.

Here are some of Julia's ideas for a put down routine:

Morning nap—Tone down your voice, give cuddles and tell the baby that it is sleepy time. Sing a lullaby and play sleepy music, perhaps using a teddy with pull cord, and then cozily tuck baby into the crib. A bunny or soft blankie is helpful to soothe them. Kiss and calmly stroke her and say good night. Go quietly and calmly out of the room and close the door smoothly. If she is upset, let her cry for perhaps five minutes at first, then go in and restart the calming routine. Pick her up and cuddle all over again, just to confirm it is alright. It does not have to take long; a few minutes is good. If she cries again, let her go for ten minutes. Often she will figure it out and go to sleep. It is true that sometimes there are personalities who are more difficult to soothe. This is where a soft blankie or bunny can be a wonderful help.

Afternoon nap—Julia will give the baby a bottle on the couch, laying her down with her bunny and tucked in cozily. After she is finished, she takes her upstairs and puts her in bed with the same song as in the morning nap if she needs it, making the blankets nice and tight, kissing her and leaving the room. She does not put the baby to sleep with a bottle in order to prevent cavities.

Night bedtime—She can read, play, have her bath, breast feed and brush her teeth if she has any. Then, as in the morning nap, do the same routine of cuddling/rocking, singing, tucking into bed with cozy blankets, prayers, kisses and reassuring words such as "It's time for sleep, Honey, sweet dreams" and so on. Babies are smart. We often underestimate them and think they will not understand, but they do. They especially understand our tone of voice. Reassuring is very important.

Soothers

Soothers can definitely pacify the baby while waiting a few minutes to feed. A few things to keep in mind are:

- try to give soothers sparingly, only when needed

- never give the soother to get baby to sleep as this will start a routine of baby waking and wanting the soother put back in

At first Julia did use a soother, but soon found it better that the baby sucked his own fingers. This is because a soother will fall out and the baby will cry until it is put back in. She recounts that it took her until the sixth baby to figure this out. Both her sixth and seventh babies sucked two fingers. She remembers her Mom encouraging this, but never thought seriously about doing it. It may be less of a risk of buck teeth as compared to a soother or a thumb, but that is a question to ask your dentist.

Waking at Night

At one month after birth, our sixth was up once during the night still. I emailed Julia asking for advice on how to help the baby along. At that time, the baby was breastfeeding at approximately the following times: 3:00 am, 9:30 am, 2:00 pm, 6:00 pm, and 9:45 pm.

Julia had this to say:

> If she wakes at 4:00 am or so, feed her. Then, I would try to offset this pattern by starting your first morning feed at 6:30 am. This will be the base feed. Then feed at 10:00 am, 2:00 pm, 6:00 pm and 10:00 pm. After that, see if you can stretch that 4:00 am feed to 4:30 or 5:00 am. Once the feed is at 5:00 am, that will become your base feed and you can work the other feeds to be around 9:30 am, 1:45 pm, 6:00 pm, 9:45 pm. It is important to set the day schedule first.

I took that advice and started a base feed at 6:30 am. The pattern of the baby waking in the middle of the night continued, some nights even at 1:00 am. Upon speaking to Julia again, she told me to focus on making sure the baby had a longer awake time before the last feed.

Looking at what was happening with the baby, I realized that, yes, she was awake for most of the hours between 6:00 and 10:00 pm, but tended to have a nap of about 45 minutes around 8:45–9:30 pm. Bringing her nap down to 8:00 pm allowed a longer stretch before her last feed and eventually lengthened her night time sleep.

The baby sleeping through the night was not an automatic thing. It took a while before she dropped that middle of the night feed. But, that is okay. I just kept working at it and focusing on what the baby needed and eventually she did sleep through the night. I know that working together with the baby, seeing what she needed and guiding her helped smooth out the bumps on the road.

Weaning From a Soother

A friend of mine once asked me how she could wean her 11 month old who would wake five times in the night wanting his soother. Julia advised the following:

- Lose the soother, cold turkey.

- Talk to baby and explain the situation.

- Try to give baby a soft blanky to go to bed with and for naps.

- A musical bear that you wind up to play before sleep times is a good routine to alert the baby that it is time to sleep.

The crying may last up to three nights. Follow this pattern to progress through the nights:

- On the first night, wait a few minutes then go in and hold him for a little cuddle and tell him it is time to sleep, no more crying, mommy loves you and so on.

- Play the music, give him the soft blanky.

- On the second time, wait a bit longer. This time just pat him and say, "It's ok, it is time to sleep, no more crying and waking Mama up." Play the music.

- On the third time, wait up to 15 minutes, tell them Daddy is sleeping, brothers and sisters are sleeping and you—baby—need to sleep, Mama needs to sleep, so no more crying, God Bless.

- Stroke the baby with circular motions on the forehead and hair. My mother-in-law does this and finds it effective.

- Fourth, try to let the little one figure out that this is not working the way he would like, so he might as well go to sleep. Let them go longer than 15 minutes, up to 20 minutes now. You have to be consistent over the next days. It will be the most effective way.

Sample
Feeding Chart

DATE: _____

Feeds: (write start time)						
e.g.						
4:00 am	7:00 am	11:00 am	2:00 pm	5:00 pm	9:00 pm	
Sleeps:						
e.g.	9:00 am–10:30 am	1:00 pm–3:00 pm		6:00 pm–7:00 pm		

DATE: _____

Feeds: (write start time)						
Sleeps:						

DATE: _____

Feeds: (write start time)						
Sleeps:						

DATE: _____

Feeds: (write start time)						
Sleeps:						

Testimonies

Christina

Mother of 7

The part that helped me the very most was to change my way of thinking when it came time to feed, put to sleep and keep the baby awake! The idea is that, yes, you feed your baby every three hours from the get go but when they wake up, you feed them and then you keep them awake instead of letting them fall asleep feeding! This can be difficult with newborns but with a little practice and some ingenuity it is possible—even if you are only keeping them awake for 10–15 minutes. Then you feed them every three hours but they learn to fall asleep on their own, not on the breast. I guess the light coming on was the realization that the routine really is let them sleep, feed them and then let them have wake time. The wake time does get longer as they get older and so do the times between feedings.

Erica

Mother of 6, including twins

We have 6 kids and did not do anything like this with the first two. When I was having my 3rd, I realized that we would need more sleep, so I decided to try this out. The key to making this system work for me was to follow the eat, then wake, and then sleep routine for baby. This was important because it prevented baby from being soothed to sleep while feeding and then subsequently being disturbed in the middle of sleep with gas pains. First they would feed. Then they would have a chance to get their gas out with leg exercises and "playtime." After the diaper change, I made sure that baby was given a little cuddle and then put to bed awake. This way, they learned to soothe themselves back to sleep if they woke in the night since they weren't rocked to sleep and weren't surprised or upset to discover they were in their bed if they roused a little during sleep because they went to sleep knowing where they were.

I made an addition to this schedule, though. After every feed and playtime I would hold the babies over the toilet (or even sink) and they would have a bowel movement. I started this at 4 or 5 days old and they started to have a regular 'bathroom' cycle. It took a few days of consistency to achieve a regular cycle. This prevented diaper rash, messy poops and saved on diapers.

With the twins, the schedule was really the best. Working with the babies, I got them on the same schedule so that my day was much more organized and I had time for housework as well as more time to spend with the rest of my children. Putting them in their bed awake was key since they would soothe themselves and easily fall back to sleep. If I had not worked with them in getting into this routine, they would have been on different schedules.

While we were in the midst of the sleep training and the babies would cry, one thing that helped me was to go in the room at certain time intervals, put my hand on their back and talk to them for a couple of seconds. I couldn't just let them cry so this was a good compromise.

One more note—keep in mind that you may have to retrain when things like teething, sickness and growth spurts occur.

Frances

*Mom of 7 and blogger at **ILoveMyGrowingFamily.com***

I was introduced to this method after my sixth child and decided to try it. In order to be a cheerful and joyful mom one needs sleep. After two months I found my daughter sleeping through the night.

However, when my seventh child came I found that after a month she was already sleeping through the night! I was thrilled until I ended up with mastitis! It is important to gradually wean baby off the night feed when one's milk flow is consistent. I was flexible with each child and with the simple instructions I was able to be a better wife and mom due to following the basic premise of a parent directed feeding schedule. I noticed the kids felt more secure and calmer knowing their mom was in charge of when they ate and they didn't need to cry to be fed. I would encourage all moms to try this method and make modifications for each child as all children are different and unique.

Joanna

Julia's sister, mother of 6 and a doctor

I think the advice that Julia gave me that is paramount to having a sleeping baby is having the baby fall asleep in their own bed. I would always change their diaper after they feed and so they are awake when I put them in their bed. That way they don't get scared when they wake at night. They know the environment hasn't changed and they are still in a safe spot. Often they just fall back to sleep then. I'm a big believer in cuddling and soothing them while they are lying in their beds trying to fall asleep as opposed to carrying them around. I think that helps.

I start helping them to fall asleep in their own bed right away. It doesn't have to be every nap (sometimes you're out and it ends up in the stroller or car seat) but the majority of the time. My babies (most babies) are a little jaundiced in the first couple of weeks which makes them super sleepy. I think that is God's gift to make it easier to get acquainted with the bed and a routine. Once that 2 week window of opportunity is done they are much more verbal about any change to the routine. My friends for example had family visiting for the first 3 weeks so the baby was constantly held. Once their family left, they discovered that they could not put the baby down without her screaming. The baby was terrified by this new experience. That first week or two is critical to introduce them to what to expect.

Lisa

Mother of 5, including twins

Short term pain = long term gain. I remember it being a bit tough at first but then the babies slept so well!! More sleep for mamma = happy mamma = happy family!

Marianne

Mother of 2

I tried the "system" because I was exhausted from lack of sleep and I remember having difficulties with my first born for a couple of years before he slept through the night. So I thought, "Why not?" The first few nights were a little scary for me but my daughter quite easily fell into the "system" and started sleeping through the night in about a week. My challenge however is if they fall out of their routine when they are older. How do you get back into a routine?

Valentina had an ear infection and my doctor told me to pick her up whenever she cried and nurse her because it would help her ear infection, so consequently Valentina's routine was broken. I am starting again and hoping the system will work once again. Moms with a new baby need to hear the advice from other moms that have done this. The support system of family and friends is crucial. Your information and encouragement helped me try so... Thanks. Put the advice in a book and get it out there.

Odilia

Mother of 6

We cannot fully follow the schedule (i.e. we sleep with our babies due to limited space in our townhouse), but I find many of the techniques in the notes quite useful to follow. We started implementing Julia's advice with our fourth child. For example, what I practice often is not picking up our babies right away when they cry. A lot of the times they fall back to sleep by themselves anyway. Also, we try to slowly get our babies on a feeding schedule by keeping the babies awake before the last feed and stretching out the feeds as Julia suggests. One way I do this is to let my husband and older children play with or pick up the baby.

Julia's method helps me realize that I do not need to feed the baby every time he cries. I find that it is all right for the baby to cry a bit—it's good to exercise the lungs.

Once babies have a regular feeding schedule, they are more settled. They know when they need to be fed and when they need to sleep. They have a routine and know what to expect; their routine fits very well into the family routine.

Pamela

Mother of 4

With my first child, I used Elizabeth Pantley's, "The No-Cry Sleep Solution." The baby would wake up, I would feed him immediately, he would be awake for an hour or so, then sleep. He would wake up or I would wake him at the three hour mark. This system worked well, so well that when we traveled with the baby to Europe, he had no troubles with jet-lag as he was on a set three hour schedule—I could set the clock on his routine. However, as he grew older and bigger, his time between feedings did not expand, nor did his length of sleeping periods at night. Still three hours, like clock-work. When I had my second child, I attempted this similar method to him, however he was colicky. He would cry and bunch up his legs. As I had an older, very active toddler running around, I gave up this method and began demand feeding. It was a cycle. The baby would cry, I would feed him, he would fall asleep quickly as I fed him, so he did not get a full feed, then he would wake up very easily and not be happy, so the cycle would start again. He would spit up a fair bit, too. I needed to have antibiotics prior to giving birth. In retrospect, I would have increased my post-birth pro-biotic intake or explored a pre-biotic or pro-biotic for the baby. Even with all these demand feeds, the baby was low on the weight gain and growth charts, so my doctor monitored him more frequently during the first 12 months.

When I was expecting my third child, I spoke with Ida about breast feeding and she told me about the approach of having the baby awake for a time, then feeding the baby once he is tired, keeping the baby awake during feeding (tickling toes), to ensure a good feed. Then, once the baby is fed, putting him down for a nap, possibly awake so he can get used to soothing himself. I think I generally tried to feed on both sides (10–15 minutes each, making sure I was empty on the first side, then starting on the second side for the next feeding). This method also offered a window of where to stretch the time between feedings. So when the baby was awake, he could be played with or distracted a little—even 5 minutes—to extend the time between feedings.

This "new" breast feeding technique helped out so much. Before the last feed at night, the baby would be awake for an hour or so, then my husband would bathe the baby while I had time with the other children. Often the baby may not be very happy at this point, but then after being awake and having a bath, I would feed him. He would feed very well and have a good sleep. **I would try to be ready for bed before that last feed, so that I could go right to bed too in hopes of having a solid few hours of sleep**. I remember he would sleep very well at night and during the day. And when he woke up, he would be happy and alert for a time before being fed again.

Again I used this method with my fourth child. The baby easily adapted to the routine and she would sleep well until early morning, at which point I would get up, feed her and then I was ready to get up for the day.

Patricia

Mother of 3, including twins

Oh, yes, I did Julia's method! It was great. It worked perfectly for triples. I had a daughter who was a one year old and newborn twin babies. I did it exactly as Julia said and then passed the method on to my sister in law with two kids.

The key of it all is consistency, persistency and do not give up!!! Take one day at a time. Keep in mind that the key as a mother is to give always so that you are the foundation for your family. As a mother you go through different stages so you have to enjoy each moment with them. Invest your time in the formation of your kids especially from 0 to 13... you will never regret it! This is the key to success later on. It will get easier.

Most importantly, the best gift for your kids is not toys or electronics but a brother or sister so that they support each other later on.

Patti

Mother of 2

I am so grateful for Julia's help with our second child's sleeping plan. We really didn't have a concrete plan for our first born and so we tried all kinds of different ways to get him to sleep. Usually it was trouble shooting his constant wakings in the middle of the night. When we were expecting our second child we decided that we could not do this with our next baby! Through friends I heard about Julia's sleeping plan. By using Julia's sleeping plan with our second child things went quite differently. We were able to get her to sleep through the night after 6 weeks! I would highly recommend using Julia's sleeping plan for your baby. It would greatly benefit family life as a good night's sleep is very important to the well being of each family member!

Rosana

Mother of 2

We bottle fed Luke (my milk never did come in). Since it takes their little bodies longer to digest formula rather than breast milk, we found that it is a little easier to stretch the feeds out. When Luke was almost 6 weeks, he worked his way into 4 feeds per day. He was steadily gaining weight as well (we weighed him frequently) so since he was happy with the 4 feeds then we just stuck with that.

We did use a soother as a tool to stretch him out (letting baby cry a little is good for them too) and always put him to bed awake so he got used to putting himself to sleep on his own. Swaddling is key as well. I hear so many moms say that their baby hates to be swaddled so they don't do it. Babies are used to being in tight quarters in your tummy and I find that they may squirm a little when first swaddled but it very quickly relaxes them.

The main thing I have learned from the schedule is that babies sleep how they eat. If mums are feeding their babes every 2 hours (what I call snacking) then the babe is only taking very short cat naps. This scenario does not work for mum or baby. Mums must focus on giving baby a full feed every time.

Reflections

In relation to the ideas on babies and sleep, the following personal reflections are the interior light defining the exterior practice.

My Story

by Ida Gazzola

My husband and I have six girls and one boy. Like most modern moms, I gave birth to the first with only a fuzzy idea of what having a baby would really be like. I had a collection of snippets of advice from a variety of sources, along with a few books. This jumble of oral and written advice formed the basis for my first attempt at baby care. Our eldest daughter turned out to be a fairly good sleeper on her own. According to the doctor, this was due in part to the bump on her head (caused by her entry into the world) and a touch of jaundice. Nonetheless, I followed a well-meaning nurse's advice and set my alarm every night and woke the baby up every three hours to feed her! When I went to my doctor for the baby's first week check up, I asked her how long I had to keep setting my alarm. Her eyes widened as she said, "You're setting your alarm? Don't set your alarm! Let the baby sleep."

Almost two years later, daughter number two came along. At that time, our eldest was going through a nightmare phase. She would wake up after a bad dream ("there are sharks swimming in my room") and stay awake for hours... and hours.... So, that was my excuse for feeding the baby every time she made a squeak. It seemed a lot easier to feed the baby than to stay awake for hours with a whiny two-year-old. Doing this established a pattern of nightly feeds or waking that lasted until after she was one year old. I remember after her first birthday party, climbing into bed and saying to my husband, "She's one now! We shouldn't be so tired still!"

During the pregnancy with our next girl, underneath our happiness in welcoming a new little life, lurked a specter. It was the specter of the year of sleeplessness we endured with the last baby. Would it happen again? Could we handle it? Maybe there was a way we could prevent it. Then I remembered, even with my fuzzy mommy's brain, my friend, Julia, who said her babies would sleep through the night at one month. She had emailed me her ideas years before, but for one reason or another, I had not tried to put them into practice. This time, I decided, would be different. For the sake of my family and to maintain sanity in the household, I would give her ideas my best shot. And, it worked! Baby girl number three was sleeping 10.5 hours every single night starting October 11, 2006 (2 months and 2 days after her birth). I think I'll always remember that date because it really was a source of joy for me. I woke up after a good night's sleep and thought, "I have to buy Julia a present." And then, every night after that the baby just kept sleeping through the night. It wasn't a fluke!

So, needless to say, we did the same thing with baby girl number four. And, yes, she also was sleeping 10–11 hours by two months. Baby girl number five was only sleeping 8 hours by the second month. While this seemed very little to me, Julia reminded me that the babe was actually right on track according to the schedule. Hindsight allows me to see that because I was physically weaker after this birth, I was also slower in implementing the schedule compared to the other 2 babies. With the first two babies, I had actually been a bit ahead of the game. Also, now that she is older, I can see how her little personality was already coming out as a newborn. She has a quiet, but strong personality that is in special need of the comfort of Momma. As a newborn, it seemed that she didn't want me to leave the room when it was sleep time. I couldn't understand it since the others had not been like that. But, in light of her personality, it all makes sense now!

As for the sixth girl, she was pretty much right on track with her sleeping—not ahead of the game, but not behind either. The lesson to be learned here is that, even with a much weakened physical state, such as having had a caesarean or extreme exhaustion, Julia's schedule is still do-able.

When my little boy came along, I was ready for a challenge! I had reread all of Julia's info and felt prepared. However, God always gives us what we can handle and it appears that I couldn't handle much of a challenge at all! Our baby boy actually slept through the night until 4:30 am right off the bat (he had two or three 2:30 am wakings, but that's it). We felt extremely blessed in more ways than one.

Motherhood

"[Motherhood is] the biggest gamble in the world. It is the glorious life force. It's huge and scary—it's an act of infinite optimism." —Gilda Radner

Only a woman who is not a mother is able to purely romanticize motherhood. Once a woman's motherhood begins, with the baby growing inside her, the other, non-romantic side emerges. This side can be scary, with so many things that could go wrong, and countless physical mishaps or worse.... Then, there is the fact that every child is his own person. That means that he can freely make wrong decisions and hurt himself or others.

So, being a mother means accepting two contradictory positions. Positive and negative, life and death—these live side by side. This fact is true for any living human being, but mothers, through their intense closeness with their child, have a sort of magnifying glass on this aspect of existence.

One Thanksgiving weekend, I picked up the kids from school and was thinking how they were all particularly grumpy. When we arrived home, our two-year-old, choking on a piece of apple, stopped breathing and became as limp as a rag doll. Turning her upside down with a few quick hits to her back dislodged the apple.

This incident turned sourness into sweetness and our family rejoiced. Any disagreements between the siblings vanished. As a family, we cheered for the rescued one and hugged each other, glad that we were alive and together. As one young daughter reflected, "Before this, we were grumpy. Now we are happy!" Joy came out of trial.

Motherhood is like this. It is this. Joys and trials. Labour and love. We labour to birth our children and then we labour to raise them. And, love is woven throughout.

Another feature of motherhood that is both a joy and a trial is the mental and emotional aspect. It is a source of growth as well as a challenge. We simultaneously have to deal with our own physical and emotional issues while helping our children with theirs. It has happened a number of times that, just as I have been grappling with these issues, I will run into a mom who has grown children who will say to me, "Enjoy them while they are young." This statement has given me pause.

How do you enjoy your children when they are fighting each other and being disobedient? When they are screaming at the top of their lungs and can only hear you if you scream louder than they? This is not enjoyment. Forget it. Let us not 'enjoy them while they are young.' Instead, let us try to live each moment fully. Some of those moments are full of chaos and others are full of sweetness. The challenge is to turn the chaos into order, where peace and calm reign, where things are the way they should be. How can we use our God-given creativity to turn a situation around? Or at least to bring it down to a simmer? Can we, with a gentle forcefulness, take our daughter's shoulder and say with a confident smile, "I love you and I want you to be happy. You are strong and capable of so many things. So, be happy. You can do it." Then, talk to her; have her tell you what is worrying her and let her discover how she can rise above it.

One experienced mother told me, "When things go wrong, I have learned to say to myself—this is the way it is." Accepting things the way they are allows us to put our feelings aside and be more objective in each situation. It allows us to stop thinking, "Why am I not enjoying life?" When we do this, we turn our focus away from self and a funny thing happens: we start enjoying life. Happiness for a mother comes from focusing on our loved ones, on their day-to-day worries and joys, rejoicing, serving and loving. John Paul II encouraged women to discover their own feminine humanity. Through our motherhood, we reveal the richness and personal resources of femininity, the eternal originality of the "woman," just as she was meant to be, a person for her own sake, who discovers herself "by means of a sincere gift of self" (Mulieris Dignitatem, 11).

Marriage

"You know, your Dad is number one in my life." In the context of an intimate conversation between mother and child, my mom said these words to me. I gazed at the face I loved so much and felt a slight sting.

Some conversations last with you for your lifetime. This was one of them. Now married with children, I have made these words my own. Daddy does come before baby (or babies as the case may be) and that's the way it should be! As a child I did not understand it, but as an adult and wife, I am convinced of it.

Little children are so helpless, so completely needy—it seems they have to come before a grown man who can take care of himself. Caring for a child's physical needs is a huge part of being a mom. We definitely focus more on our child's bodily needs than on our husband's (he can dress/shower/feed himself). But more time spent taking care of our child is not the same as putting him or her before our husband. My husband does come before my children, with the children being such a close second that they are squished up beside him in this line up of priorities. And, I, in turn am number one for him. We are a team in this adventure of marriage and parenting. We are more than a team, since we have made a lifelong commitment of love to each other. We have given ourselves completely to each other so that, while remaining individuals, we are joined spiritually in an unbreakable bond. Even we cannot break this bond (let's face it; in life some things are not reversible).

But, if two people have made a commitment and feel that they want to change their mind, should they not be able to? Marriage is indissoluble because it is based on Love. People are made with a desire for love, and for some, this means marriage. We did not choose to have this desire for love, but it was a gift that was given to us, that came from outside of us. Marriage is special and unique since the persons desiring it want to be united for life and to give themselves in a complete way that is just not possible in other relationships. This is very nicely illustrated by the conjugal act. And this physical giving, besides uniting the couple, may result in the creation of a new life. What a miracle!

The word 'unity' in marriage may conjure up images of the romantic, fairy tale ideals we had before we were married and reality hit. Or it may make us think of being tied down a bit, of lacking freedom.

Despite not being the overly emotional type, when we were engaged and first married, my eyes used to well up upon reading St Paul's famous Hymn to Love which tells us that without love, we are nothing. We love when we are patient and kind, making allowances for others, enduring whatever comes our way.

I place my own life and marriage before St Paul's images of Love. Love is a gift that comes from outside of us, from a power greater than ours. So, if we have not conformed to the true image of Love, we can make up our mind to do so at any time. When our marriage shows signs of selfishness or impatience that does not mean we don't have Love. It means we did not choose love at one point, but Love is still there for us to choose again. It is up to us.

How a Good Marriage Affects our Children

Educator and author James Stenson wrote: Every time you kiss your wife in front of the children, you are, in effect, kissing each of them in turn.
(ParentLeadership.com Discipline: What works and Why)

What a beautiful statement. Children love unity. When I think to my own childhood, I realize that I was fortunate to have parents who rarely fought. In fact, I can only think of a handful of times. I clearly remember the anxious feeling in the pit of my stomach. Once when I heard some arguing, I went to the room where they were and slammed the door. I was very happy to hear some laughter after that! (I tried it again only once more as my dad did not take kindly to the encore.)

This is human nature. Children find security in their parents and in the unity of their parent's marriage. The closer we are to our husband, the closer our kids will feel to us. Our unity deeply impacts the entire family. Have you noticed how children feel when one spouse says an angry or sarcastic word to the other? They may each react differently (e.g. taking one spouse's side or feeling sad or angry), but the predominant reaction is always negative.

Contrast that with children's reaction to the small tokens of affection between yourself and your husband. Sometimes the children may even be embarrassed (especially at certain very self conscious stages), but they are always embarrassed with a smile. So, let us spur ourselves on to work on our marriage—to have those discussions that need to happen, to spend some quality time with our spouse, and to remember his good qualities (there are many!) when his defects seem to have overshadowed them.

What's the Point in Having More Children?

Have you ever had someone ask you, fairly soon after you've given birth, "So, are you going to have more?" Only the Imp of the Perverse (to quote Poe), would induce someone to ask such a question. In case you are not familiar with that Imp, he is what 'makes' us do that thing that we know is ridiculous, scary, or dangerous.

The Imp of the Perverse knows that if he asks you this question precisely at the moment of extreme exhaustion or difficulty, you will make a statement based on your overwhelming feelings. The most oft repeated reply to this question in our culture is, "I'm done!"

Now imagine you are being asked that question and you are able to take all those heavy feelings and throw them aside for a moment. You may have various answers to that question. We can say 'no' for some very good reasons (mental or physical medical issues, extreme monetary troubles, spouse not open to discussion) or not so good ones (I like my 'toys,' fear of what could be, disruption of the way my life is now). But, the 'no' side is not what we are talking about now.

Going to the deepest, most fundamental reason for saying yes, we arrive at **faith**. I know what you are thinking: here is a person who is having more children because they think God wants them to. Yes and no.

'Faith' induces someone to have children because they believe time will prove this to be the right thing to do. It takes a daring, human kind of faith to believe that the logic of convenience (what is easier in the here and now) will be overturned by the counter-cultural idea of trusting in our bodies' natural way of working. Flipping it 180 degrees, that means that we don't trust in devices/procedures/drugs that work against our nature, against the way we were made.

Long before I met my husband and before I had made a personal commitment to any faith, I sat down (literally) and thought long and hard about some issues, contraception and the purpose of sex being two of them. I wanted to strip them down to their bare bones, to examine them objectively, without the distortion of a cloud of emotions or physical sensations. What are they really for? Sex brings two people closer together and can result in a new life. Contraception artificially prevents a natural process and puts a barrier between the love of the couple. Therefore, contraception is out and sex is in, provided there is a lifelong commitment. Logic brings a person to this conclusion and faith helps one to live it.

We have faith in our marriage vows where we gave ourselves completely to our spouse. We trust him with that most intimate, sacred part of us—and a huge part of that includes the ability to participate in creation. This act unites us ever more deeply and, once in a while, may result in a new life. This new life is one of the greatest gifts we can ever receive.

While we are recipients of this gift of our children, simultaneously, we are givers. We gift our children with siblings. Siblings are the best present a parent can give to their children—far superior to anything material. Siblings are lifelong companions that are with us through thick and thin. They are always there to call on for help and support. Once the parents are gone, they will journey with us for most of our life. With siblings there is always trust and loyalty.

More children also allow each member of the family to become a better person through countless opportunities to develop strength of character. Generosity, trust, respect, order, the ability to persevere, empathy, understanding others, patience, forgiveness... Basically, all the traits that we uphold as honourable are much easier to foster when children grow up in a large family, where **we**, the parent, are not the main attraction and there are many that need our love, care, and elbow grease to get all the chores done. Our heart enlarges because more children equals more love.

On a deeper level, the insight of a friend of mine really made me think. She said that having children is not for **us**, it is for **them** (the kids). By having more children, we will indeed be more accomplished and fulfilled and while that is a result, it should not be the main reason for having more kids. Each and every child is a unique person that, when raised well, finds his/her own fulfillment through enriching society. We have children because they deserve to have life and experience love and fulfillment and this is only possible with our procreative cooperation. This gift of life and the ability to love is a remarkable gift that each of us has received and has the capacity to pass on to others—first of all, our children.

Maintaining Sanity in the Midst of Tiredness and Difficulties

Wanting to be happy is part of being human. Yet, there are times in our lives when we feel unhappy or dissatisfied. Most likely we did not envision the physical demands parenthood would place upon us. Once as a young, single woman and working as a gardener, I saw through the windows of a home a living room in which young children obviously played. The home was neat and tidy, with a small amount of colourful toys strewn tidily around so as to be more of a decoration than a mess. Looking in from the green, sunny garden, the home seemed quiet and peaceful. I did not think at that time of the fact that the children were absent. My romantic vision of parenting was like this: all of the joys and cuteness of the children without any of the screaming, misbehaviour, and middle of the night demands; the enjoyment of work in the home, not knowing that once you got one room looking beautiful, two others would be made into bigger messes. The vision of the dutiful, smiling mom stirring a pot on the stove with appreciative children waiting in the wings for dinner became tempered with low blood sugar induced misbehaviour (including my own!)

Our culture tends to equate reality with how a person feels when this is often not the case. For example, if love were simply a feeling, I daresay there would not be one marriage that would last. If our feelings dictated our actions, children would have to get used to their parents not coming to their aid in the wee hours.

Fortunately, we are bigger than our feelings. Love is a choice. It is thinking of others when we may not feel like it. It is desiring the best for those around us, starting with our own family. And this desire is present and compatible with completely negative feelings.

Below is a collection of practical tips to aid in regaining our inner peace.

1. **Get enough sleep (and take care of your health)**

   The wisest man I know told me that 75% of family problems are caused by lack of sleep. The more sleep challenges I endure, the more I agree with this. One idea that he suggested to a close friend of mine was to do a 'sleep-exchange' where two mothers take turns watching the others children so that one of them can take a nap. Another possibility is for a friend to have your children over for a play date while you nap.

Besides sleep deprivation, feeling exhausted can also be the result of physical factors. A periodic check up at the doctor can tell you if this is the case.

2. Consider the meaning of life

The big picture is also what we need to consider when our four walls are closing in on us. Pope Francis recently told us in his weekly audience that each new child is a new vocation. The word vocation comes from Latin meaning 'a call.' It is a path God gives us that, when traveled well, leads us more directly to him. In the family, our first vocation is our husband and then each child thereafter. So, how many vocations do we have? 2 or 5 or 7? How amazing to think that my husband and my baby are my mission, my life's work, and this mission is carried out through small acts of love each day.

3. Enrich yourself

In discussing this, my 11 year old told me, "You could read a book or do activities that you like that are restful but not complicated." Other ideas could be to: go for a walk, call a friend, attend a talk, research a topic of interest, pray, play a board game, smile more, and say no to too many invitations.

Improving our professional formation enriches us and those around us. Most of us have multiple professions—wife, mother, homemaker or employee. In all of these areas it is important that we keep up to date and constantly learn how to improve. This may take the form of formal training or sporadic reading of literature to improve our parental or homemaking skills. The benefits are really enormous—heightened efficiency and order, problems more easily solved and greater peace of mind and confidence since we will not suffer from that 'flying by the seat of our pants' feeling so often.

4. Be a proactive parent

My husband and I went to a talk by a family therapist and father of 9 girls. He and his wife meet weekly with each child and help them see 1) where they need to improve and 2) what practical baby steps they can take towards this goal.

Growth as a person is arguably more important than doing well at school, piano, or other activities. In fact, when one tackles the main weak area in one's life, that improvement fosters growth in all areas. For example, focusing on keeping her room clean helped one of my daughters to have more free time and to be less grouchy since she no longer had the inner conflict of disliking a messy room but refusing to clean it.

Family meetings are another great way to foster family unity and personal responsibility. Parenting courses or talks, books and articles can also give us some ideas of how to make life in the home run more smoothly.

5. Regular exercise

As Julia says, taking care of our physical side is as important as enriching our brain. The Canada food guide recommends adults get 2.5 hours of exercise per week. This does not have to be all at once and can be a goal we build towards. Google "Canada food guide exercise" for a long list of ways to easily incorporate exercise into your daily life. A great idea that also contributes to family bonding is to do sport as a family—e.g. skiing, swimming, hiking or tennis.

6. Relax with your husband

This is extremely important. Since the couple is the backbone of the family, time together is needed to maintain and grow that relationship. I know parents of 9 children who used to have a weekly date, sometimes overnight. My husband and I cannot manage once a week, but do make a point of short, but sweet once a month dates.

A mom of an autistic child once told me that it was impossible for her and her husband to leave their 3 children. So, once a week, they would feed the kids and put on a movie for them. Then they would open a bottle of wine, leisurely make a gourmet meal and eat it in the candlelit dining room. The kids knew they could not cross the imaginary line of the doorway and so got used to giving mom and dad their time together.

Daily or almost daily time together is important to many couples. It could consist of an hour watching either a good show or part of a DVD or even going for a run. Love is creative! There is sure to be some way to get that time together.

Positive Parenting

by Julia Dee

Our children are God's children first. God is their Creator. He designed them beautifully and entrusts them to us as a gift.

Positive Parenting starts from the beginning of parenthood, seeing the child as a gift and discovering their needs and preferences. When your child has done something well, do not praise <u>them</u>, but instead <u>praise the action or deed</u> that they did well. For example, say, "Well done, Sally, you put your shoes back and you are becoming orderly," instead of saying, "Good girl." As parents we have to continue educating our children in the virtues they need to practice and acquire. We can do this in those moments of good behavior by labeling the virtue they just carried out—for example, being orderly or generous or being cheerful with a smile. This is educating the child by stating what the virtue is and pointing out what they are to strive for. Make a big deal of the good things the child does, even if they are little things. It takes a conscious effort to notice those little achievements of your child and the small areas they are struggling in.

Challenge them, "Wonderful, see how you feel, Sally, when you share?" Your child will notice you praising the positive behaviour. When your child gets older then you can help him see how his good behavior helps the others or helps you as a mother. This also teaches the child to develop good values such as modesty, elegance in dress, diligence, perseverance, gratitude, etc.

A child will act up or have a tantrum when they need attention. They need to be loved and each child needs love in a unique way—your job is to find out what is their most receptive way to receive love. Physical affection, a positive word, time spent helping them with a task, time spent with the child—a sport, fun outing, a gift. I recommend the book *The Five Love Languages of Children*, by Gary Chapman.

Children are so smart. They know they will get your attention most effectively when they do something bad or crazy. Do not react with heated emotion. Deal with the situation calmly without feeding the frenzy as this is ineffective and causes further harm. In heat of the moment, resist pointing out their negative behavior. You will regret what you say. Take a deep breath and stay ultra calm while dealing with the situation. On a positive note, start noticing the good that they do in little things and make a big deal of these moments. The child will then seek your attention by doing good things! Wouldn't that be perfect?!

If your child (especially when they are under three years old) is having a bad behavior moment, distraction is the best technique to change the child's behavior. If they are stuck on a toy and can't have it at the moment, offer a different toy or move to another area of the house or take them to the window and look for birdies, etc. My husband would take them for a walk in the garden and draw their attention to the flowers. Magic.

Take a deep breath if you have to. Love and calmness will win the child over. When one of mine is constantly making havoc with his/her siblings, this is my red flag. This one needs more love. I need to spend more one-on-one time with him—cuddling, talking or laughing together. Make him feel appreciated by you. When the child is older than 4 years old, wait until after the incident when the atmosphere is calm or before going to bed to talk about the incident. Find or create a quiet moment with your child and help them bring up what happened earlier and what went wrong. Question them as to how they could have handled this situation better. Ask them how they think their friend felt when they behaved badly. Perhaps there is an apology that is needed.

Another reason for "bad behavior," especially for boys is sometimes just curiosity. Most often the child does not have a bad intention. They just want to see how something works or what it feels like (ditch dirt from head to toe!) or how fast they can take all the clothes off the hangers. Kids do not think things through. We have to teach them this when we have settled down and at a quiet moment. Often husbands will have a different and objective approach or understanding of the situation.

One last thought to help you develop the positive parenting approach. Near the end of the day, analyze the incidences that occurred and make resolutions for the next day. We parents are in training, too! Recognizing the good things that happen will improve your own outlook on life and positively impact your relationships with the kids and with everyone around you.

Resources

Below are just a few of the resources we have found to be helpful in relation to our job as spouse, parent, and homemaker.

Books

Martin, Jose M. editor. *Family Virtues: A Guide to Effective Parenting*. Scepter Publishers, 2015. (one of the best books on parenting!)

Mullins, Andrew. *Parenting for Character—Equipping Your Child for Life*. Finch Publishing Pty, 2005.

Isaacs, David. *Character Building: A Guide for Parents and Teachers*. Four Courts Press, 2001.

Meeker, Meg. *Strong Fathers, Strong Daughters: 10 Secrets Every Father Should Know*. Ballantine Books, 2007.

Nelson, Jane. *Positive Discipline*. Ballantine Books, 2006.

Stenson, James. *Compass: A Handbook on Parent Leadership*. Scepter Publishers, 2003. (see his website!)

Meeker, Meg. *Strong Mothers, Strong Sons: Lessons Mothers Need to Raise Extraordinary Men*. Ballantine Books, 2014.

Armstrong, Patti & Thomas, Theresa. *Big Hearted: Inspiring Stories from Everyday Families*. Scepter Publishers, 2013.

Cooney, Mary. *Evangelizing Our Children with Joy*. Scepter Publishers, 2017.

Websites

ParentLeadership.com - James B. Stenson

5LoveLanguages.com - Improving relationships

10Kids.com - Parenting, homemaking, marriage, tons of resources

ScepterPublishers.org - Go to 'Parenting, Marriage, and Family' collection

MercatorNet.com - Topical issues, book reviews

MovieGuide.org - Family guide to movies, entertainment

RosaWhatsYourSecret.com - Raising a large family with love

DeLibris.org - Book reviews

PluggedIn.ca - Reviews for movies, TV, books, games

CommonSenseMedia.org - Media reviews, resources for parents

TheFamilyDinnerProject.org - Food, fun, conversation for families

The Humanum Series Videos on Vimeo.com - Six extraordinary 15-minute videos on marriage and the family. In the words of one young mom, "It changed my life!" Available for rent or purchase.

RaisedToLove.com - Parenting and virtues

EastOfCrazyLand.com - Adventures in parenting. Some beautiful thoughts on baby loss.

ILoveMyGrowingFamily.com - Blog about teachable moments for parents and children

Pife.ca - Pacific Institute of Family Education—for marriage, parenting

Julia Dee

JULIA WITH HER FAMILY

Julia Dee completed her education in Sydney, Australia in Hotel and Tourism Management and dreamed of running a bed & breakfast in the mountains. Now she runs a bed, breakfast, lunch, and dinner for 10! She competed nationally in tennis and loves to back-country ski. She resides with her husband and 10 children in British Columbia, Canada.

Ida Gazzola

IDA WITH HER FAMILY

Ida Gazzola, Mom to 6 girls and 1 boy, loves the outdoors and being with her family. Before embarking on the adventure of marriage and family life, she studied English, Law, and Finance and worked in the financial industry. She resides with her family in British Columbia, Canada.